Fun with Dick and Jane

A COMMEMORATIVE COLLECTION OF STORIES

CollinsPublishers

A Division of HarperCollins*Publishers*

See Dick. See Jane. The stories of Dick and Jane taught millions of children to read with simple vocabulary, warmly drawn pictures and endearing plots. First introduced in a 1930 schoolbook published by Scott Foresman, Dick and Jane were fixtures in American education for more than forty years. Many things have changed since then. Dick and Jane have been replaced in classrooms with a wide diversity of literature. But they remain an integral part of America's story. For those millions of Americans who learned to read with Dick and Jane, and for those wanting to experience their simple charm, we're pleased to offer this sampling of classic stories.

Look

Look, look.

Oh, oh, oh.

Oh, oh.

Oh, look.

Spot

Come, Dick.

Come and see.

Come, come.

Come and see.

Come and see Spot.

Look, Spot.

Oh, look.

Look and see.

Oh, see.

Run, Spot.

Run, run, run.

Oh, oh, oh.

Funny, funny Spot.

See It Go

Jane said, "Look, look.

I see a big yellow car.

See the yellow car go."

Sally said, "I see it.

I see the big yellow car.

I want to go away in it.

I want to go away, away."

Dick said, "Look up, Sally.

You can see something.

It is red and yellow.

It can go up, up, up.

It can go away."

Sally said, "I want to go up.

I want to go up in it.

I want to go up, up, up.

I want to go up and away."

"Look, Sally," said Dick.

"Here is Father in a boat.

You can go away in it."

"Jump in, jump in," said Father.

"Jump in the big blue boat."

"We can go," said Sally.

"We can go away in a boat.

Away in a big blue boat."

A Doll for Jane

"Hello, Father," said Dick.

"Jane will have a birthday soon.

Please get a new doll for Jane.

Get a baby doll that talks.

Please get a doll that talks."

Sally said, "Oh, Mother.

Jane will have a birthday.

She will have a birthday soon.

Guess what Jane wants.

She wants a new doll.

She saw a baby doll that talks.

She wants it.

Please get a baby doll for Jane."

"Happy birthday," said Father.

"I have something for you, Jane."

"Happy birthday!" said Mother.

"Happy birthday, Jane.

I have something for you, too."

Jane said, "Thank you, Father.

Thank you, Mother.

I cannot guess what you

have for my birthday."

"Here, Jane," said Dick.

"This is something for you."

Jane ran to Dick.

"Oh, is that for me?" she said.

"Is that for my birthday, too?

I cannot guess what it is.

I will look and see."

"One, two, three," said Jane.

"Three new dolls for my birthday!

Three baby dolls that talk!

All for my birthday!

Now I have a big doll family.

Thank you, thank you, thank you.

This is a happy birthday.

A happy, happy birthday for me."

Something Blue for Puff

"Girls! Girls!" said Dick.

"Come in the house.

I want you to see something."

Pam said, "Oh, Dick!

What do you want us to see?"

"Come and find out," said Dick.

"It is something you girls will like."

Dick said, "See what Mike and I have.

This is Puff with me.

That is Spot with Mike."

Mike said, "Come here, girls.

See Spot and Puff in a little play."

"Oh, I like plays," said Sally.

"We do, too," said Pam and Penny.

Spot said, "Hello, Puff.

See my red coat.

Do you want a red coat, too?"

Puff said, "I like the red coat, Spot.

But I want a blue coat.

Maybe you can find a blue one for me."

"That is easy," said Spot.

"Look at my hat and you will see."

"Puff! Look at this!" said Spot.

"Here is a blue coat for you!"

Penny said, "Oh, that is good, Spot!

Now find coats for us!

Find a blue coat for Sally.

Find red coats for Pam and me."

ISBN:0-06-076681-6
Printed in Hong Kong